THE JOY OF
A PEANUTS CHRISTMAS

50 Years of Holiday Comics!

Hallmark
BOOKS

The Joy of a PEANUTS Christmas published in 2000 by Hallmark Cards, Inc.

Hallmark logo and Hallmark Books logo are trademarks of
Hallmark Cards, Inc., 2501 McGee, Kansas City, MO, 64141.

http://www.hallmark.com

PEANUTS is a registered trademark of United Feature Syndicate, Inc.
PEANUTS © United Feature Syndicate, Inc.
Based on the PEANUTS ® comic strip by Charles Schulz.

http://www.unitedmedia.com

Designed and produced by book soup publishing, inc., Philadelphia, PA,
with Running Press Book Publishers, Philadelphia, PA.

Cover and interior design by Susan Van Horn.

Edited by Erin Slonaker and Megan Bossuyt.

Printed in the United States.

10 9 8 7 6 5 4 3 2 1

CONTENTS

INTRODUCTION

Charles Schulz is the cartoon champion of all time. . .
He is a magician with a pencil.

—JOYCE C. HALL, FOUNDER, HALLMARK CARDS, INC.

In some way, we can all relate to the trials and tribulations,
the fun and foibles of the PEANUTS gang.

—DONALD J. HALL, CHAIRMAN, HALLMARK CARDS, INC., AND SON OF JOYCE C. HALL

PEANUTS and Hallmark have been playing on the same team for more than forty years, but unlike the ill-fated baseball team Charlie Brown valiantly captains, ours has always been a winning combination. Together we've created over one hundred different products—cards, ornaments, address books, yo-yos and even a Hallmark Hall of Fame production. Together we've shared in the joys and sorrows, the laughter and loves of the whole PEANUTS gang: Charlie Brown and Snoopy, Lucy and Linus, Sally and Schroeder, Peppermint Patty and Marcie, Franklin and Pig-Pen, Woodstock and Spike. We've seen them grow up (sort of), fall in and out of love (in a manner of speaking) and set off on adventures and journeys from Snoopy's Red Baron flights to Linus's relentless quest for the Great Pumpkin.

And we're proud to have been a part of it all.

For us, it all began on May 16, 1960, when Charles Schulz agreed to create four greeting cards for our company. Forty years and more than one hundred products later, the Schulz family and my own have become both great business partners and great friends. Sparky and I shared a love of golf, and, like Charlie Brown, we always hoped that the next game would be better.

I think PEANUTS and Hallmark get along so well because we have so much in common. We're both known for a dedication to quality. We share a commitment to family and community. And we both bring good feelings—warmth, joy, happiness and love—into the daily lives of millions. We're a perfect match. "They think a lot of times of things I wish I had thought of myself," Charles Schulz once said of our family business. "I frequently look at their cards and think, 'I wish I'd used that in my strip.'" Believe me, the feeling is mutual.

A cartoon strip, after all, tells a story—much like a card. And one of the truly magical things about PEANUTS is the way that the characters so truthfully share their emotions. Maybe that's why they work so well in greeting cards.

We've learned a lot of things about Charles Schulz and his PEANUTS gang over the years. We've learned that all PEANUTS characters are right-handed (one of our artists accidentally drew Peppermint Patty writing with her left hand). We learned that Schroeder only listens to

Beethoven (one of our designers once mistakenly drew rows and rows of music by a different composer). We learned that despite their cartoony nature, each PEANUTS character actually has a human hand (another designer once drew a character with only three fingers and a thumb).

But mostly, we've learned what millions of people around the world already know about PEANUTS—that it simply, honestly and beautifully teaches us about life. After all, despite all the gang's quarrels, trials and tribulations, they always come together when it's really important.

When Charles Schulz died in February of 2000, the world lost more than a brilliant artist, a creator of cultural icons and a national treasure. We lost a man who loved his work, who loved his family, who loved his country. We lost a man who spoke his message clearly through his beloved characters and taught us that we can all win the game if we work together, if we love, if we laugh and if we keep on trying.

Somehow, it doesn't matter that Charlie Brown never did kick that football. That he kept trying was enough.

I hope you enjoy this look back at the PEANUTS gang over the years—from the '50s through the '90s. We at Hallmark are delighted to be publishing this one-of-a-kind collection of Charles Schulz's classic Christmas strips, in honor of *The Joy of a PEANUTS Christmas*.

—DON HALL

THE '50s

December 24, 1951

December 15, 1952

January 12, 1953

December 18, 1958

February 22, 1953

CHARLIE BROWN

His dog calls him "that round-headed kid" and his friends sometimes call him "blockhead," but everyone knows him by his full name. He is Charlie Brown, the occasionally tarnished star of the gang, a born loser who

"CHRISTMAS EVE IS MY FAVORITE DAY OF THE YEAR. IT MAKES ME FEEL GOOD ABOUT EVERYTHING."

never loses hope. Even though his baseball team always loses, Lucy always pulls the football away, and his friends ridicule his Christmas tree, Charlie Brown keeps trying and always faces the coming holiday or sport season with optimism.

December 25, 1953

December 25, 1954

PIG-PEN

Pig-Pen always wanders around in a cloud—of dirt. And he leaves dirt on everything in his path. But Pig-Pen has accepted his dirtiness and is happy that way. His Christmastime snowmen may not be the cleanest snowmen in town, but at least they've got character—just like Pig-Pen.

January 6, 1955

January 13, 1955

November 21, 1957

December 21, 1959

LUCY

Lucille Van Pelt is crabby, loud, often angry, and proud of it. She makes no attempt to hide her emotions or her opinions and can be just plain mean to her brother Linus, her friends and even the neighborhood dog. She always knows the answers (she's the neighborhood psychiatrist), she's always right (no matter what the facts say), and she is always in charge (whether or not anyone wants

"I JUST NOTICED SOMETHING ABOUT THIS ROOM. THERE'S AN APPALLING LACK OF MISTLETOE."

her to be). Despite resistance from Schroeder, she continues to pursue him by hanging mistletoe at Christmas or leaning seductively on his piano.

December 31, 1956

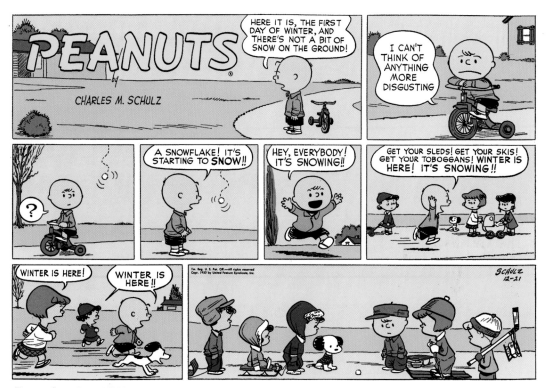

December 21, 1952

January 23, 1955

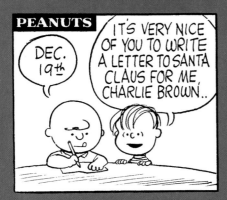

December 19, 1958

LINUS

Sucking his thumb and gripping his powder-blue blanket, Linus Van Pelt taught us about the meaning of Christmas and convinced us that the Great Pumpkin would bring us presents on Halloween. The deep thinker, he solves problems for all of the **PEANUTS** gang. His older sister Lucy

"DEAR SANTA, I AM NOT SURE WHAT I WANT FOR CHRISTMAS THIS YEAR. PERHAPS YOU SHOULD SEND ME YOUR CATALOGUE."

can't stand him, but Charlie's little sister Sally is infatuated with him. Despite an ongoing rivalry with Snoopy for the blanket, Linus always comes out on top. He is clearly wise beyond his years.

December 24, 1957

THE '60s

January 6, 1963

December 7, 1960

January 30, 1961

November 16, 1961

December 11, 1961

November 18, 1961

December 7, 1963

December 22, 1963

PEANUTS — I'M GOING TO BE A SHEPHERD IN THE CHRISTMAS PLAY, SNOOPY..

THIS IS THE PIECE I HAVE TO MEMORIZE...

"AND THERE WERE IN THE SAME COUNTRY SHEPHERDS ABIDING IN THE FIELD, KEEPING WATCH OVER THEIR FLOCK BY NIGHT."

THAT'S A GOOD LINE... I WONDER WHO WROTE IT...

December 21, 1964

PEANUTS — YOU'RE GOING TO BE IN THE CHRISTMAS PLAY, TOO, SNOOPY!

I'M GOING TO BE A SHEPHERD, AND YOU'RE GOING TO BE MY FLOCK OF SHEEP..

DO YOU THINK YOU CAN IMITATE A FLOCK OF SHEEP?

NO TROUBLE AT ALL.... ONE BEAGLE IS WORTH A WHOLE FLOCK OF SHEEP ANY TIME!

December 22, 1964

December 23, 1964

December 24, 1964

December 21, 1966

PEPPERMINT PATTY Captain

of her baseball and football teams, Peppermint Patty is a rough-and-tumble girl who would rather be on the playing field than in the classroom. She and her friends Marcie and Franklin attend a different school from Charlie Brown, but they all go to the same summer camp. Throughout the rest of the year, they see each other occasionally—for baseball and football games, as well as at Halloween and Christmas parties.

"DON'T SIGH LIKE THAT MA'AM. . . CHRISTMAS VACATION IS A LONG WAY OFF."

December 22, 1966

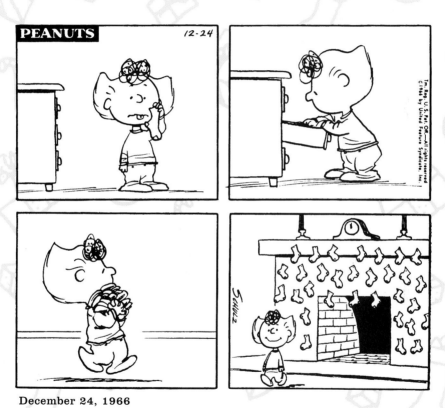

December 24, 1966

December 25, 1966

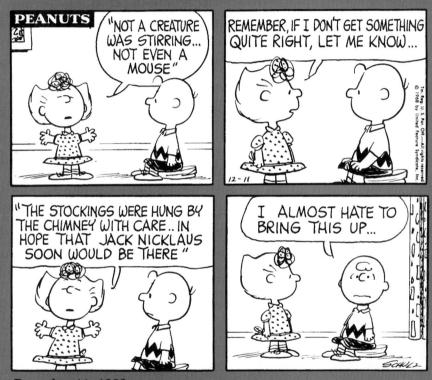

December 11, 1968

December 26, 1968

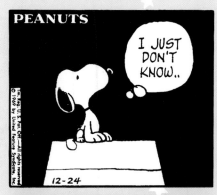

December 24, 1969

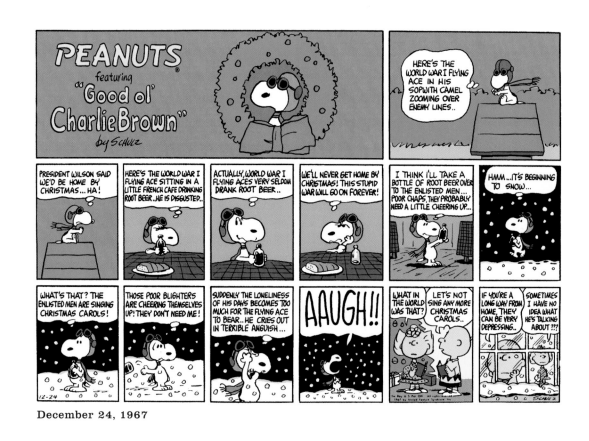

December 24, 1967

December 25, 1969

THE '70s

MUSTN'T TOUCH!!

December 26, 1971

December 18, 1972

SALLY

Sally Brown is a silly little sister to Charlie Brown. She spends most of her time making up excuses to stay home from school for a day, coercing her big brother into

"THE STOCKINGS WERE HUNG BY THE CHIMNEY WITH CARE. . IN HOPE THAT JACK NICKLAUS SOON WOULD BE THERE."

doing her homework for her, or pursuing Linus, her unrequited love, her "Sweet Babboo." Easily confused, she once wrote a school report on "Santa Claus and his Rain Gear" and thanked the wrong grandmother for her Christmas presents.

December 22, 1973

December 23, 1973

PEANUTS

MERRY CHRISTMAS, LITTLE FRIEND OF FRIENDS!

CHRISTMAS IS A GOOD DAY FOR OUR KIND...

CHRISTMAS IS FOR THE INNOCENT...

12-25

WE'RE AS INNOCENT AS THEY COME!

SCHULZ

December 25, 1973

December 10, 1976

January 6, 1975

December 23, 1979

PEANUTS

HERE COMES WOODSTOCK...

HE DOESN'T KNOW I GOT HIM SOMETHING FOR CHRISTMAS

I'M GONNA SURPRISE HIM, AND HANG THIS LITTLE CANDY CANE RIGHT ON HIS NOSE...

12-25

SCHULZ

December 25, 1976

December 24, 1977

January 22, 1978

I'M WRITING A STORY FOR SCHOOL

IT'S ALL ABOUT SANTA CLAUS AND HIS RAIN GEAR

ARE YOU SURE THAT'S RIGHT?

OF COURSE, I'M SURE!

I WONDER IF THAT INCLUDES A FOLDING UMBRELLA..

WHAT'D YOU SAY?

December 18, 1978

THIS IS MY CHRISTMAS STORY..." SANTA AND HIS RAIN GEAR"

" WHEN SANTA LEFT THE NORTH POLE THAT EVENING, A GENTLE MIST WAS FALLING"

"IN HIS YELLOW SLICKER AND BIG RUBBER BOOTS, HE SET OUT ON HIS ANNUAL JOURNEY"

"IT WAS CHRISTMAS EVE, AND SOON CHILDREN AROUND THE WORLD WOULD BE HEARING THE SOUND OF SANTA AND HIS RAIN GEAR"

December 19, 1978

"LITTLE GEORGE WAS WAITING FOR SANTA TO COME"

"SUDDENLY HE HEARD THE SOUND OF SOMEONE WALKING ON THE ROOF! IT WAS A MAN IN A YELLOW SLICKER AND BIG RUBBER BOOTS!"

"'I SAW HIM!' SHOUTED LITTLE GEORGE..'I SAW SANTA AND HIS RAIN GEAR'"

DON'T SQUIRM, MA'AM, THERE'S MORE TO COME!

December 20, 1978

"THE RAIN CAME DOWN HARDER AND HARDER"

"BUT THE MAN IN THE YELLOW SLICKER AND BIG RUBBER BOOTS NEVER FALTERED"

"ANOTHER CHRISTMAS EVE HAD PASSED, AND SANTA AND HIS RAIN GEAR HAD DONE THEIR JOB! THE END"

HA HA HA! HA HA! HA HA!

December 21, 1978

WOODSTOCK

Whether his hockey team is playing on the birdbath or he's typing letters on Snoopy's behalf, Woodstock is a busy little bird. He speaks only in birdspeak, a complex language of apostrophes and gestures, and he can just as easily express his happiness as his anger. He has been known to give Snoopy birdseed for Christmas and often becomes little more than a mound of snow if he sits still too long in a snowstorm. Above all, he's Snoopy's best friend and has more love and heart than anyone else his size.

December 24, 1978

THE '80s

December 17, 1980

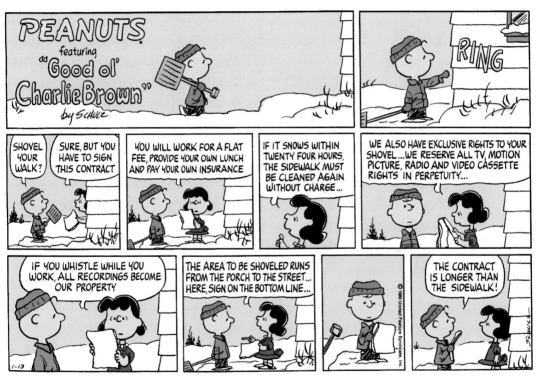

January 13, 1980

December 25, 1985

December 13, 1980

SCHROEDER

A prodigy with a toy piano, Schroeder idolizes Beethoven and cannot be bothered with much else. Much of his Christmas season is spent avoiding Lucy and mistletoe; he much prefers his favorite holiday, Beethoven's birthday. He can

"I'VE BEEN READING UP ON WINTER."

always be counted on for his musical talents, however, and is always a part of any school production.

December 18, 1981

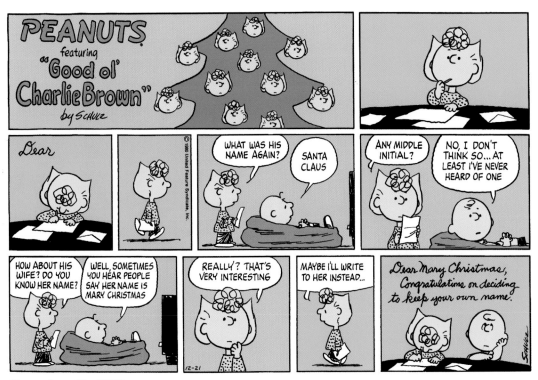

December 21, 1980

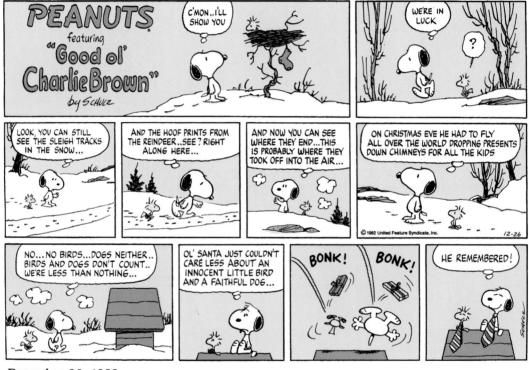

December 26, 1982

December 10, 1984

December 19, 1983

December 25, 1983

December 20, 1981

SNOOPY

Snoopy does it all—he's everything from a World War I Flying Ace to an accomplished writer to a tennis champion to a trickster. He has a weakness for root beer and pizza, often consuming so much that he spends the night atop his doghouse listening to his stomach rumble. He is protective of his best friend, Woodstock, and the two make sure to exchange Christmas presents every year. Snoopy is a true Renaissance beagle.

"ANYONE WHO WOULD FLY AROUND FROM HOUSE TO HOUSE IN A SLEIGH WITH A BUNCH OF REINDEER HAS TO BE OUT OF HIS MIND!"

December 7, 1985

December 21, 1989

November 15, 1987

December 13, 1986

MARCIE

The complete opposite of her best friend, Peppermint Patty, Marcie has both book smarts and common sense—but she is completely inept at sports. She insists on calling Peppermint Patty "Sir" in the face of all Patty's protests and is always nearby if Peppermint Patty's around. Even though she's not confident on the baseball diamond, she always participates and finds areas in which she can excel; she was Mary in the Christmas pageant.

"MY FAMILY SAID IT'S ALL RIGHT TO BELIEVE IN SANTA CLAUS, BUT NOT THE GREAT PUMPKIN."

December 25, 1988

December 20, 1989

December 19, 1989

December 19, 1986

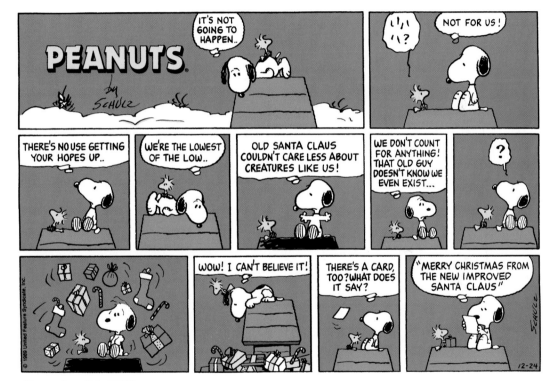

December 24, 1989

December 24, 1985

December 22, 1989

THE '90s

November 29, 1995

November 30, 1995

ALL MY CHRISTMAS CARDS CAME BACK!

THAT'S BECAUSE YOU DREW YOUR OWN STAMPS

I COPIED THEM FROM THE NEW CARTOON STAMPS

SHE DREW A BETTER POPEYE THAN THEY DID..

December 1, 1995

DO YOU THINK I'LL GET ARRESTED FOR DRAWING MY OWN STAMPS?

WELL, YOU MIGHT START LOOKING FOR A GOOD ATTORNEY..

BEFORE WE BEGIN, YOUR HONOR, MAY WE ASK IF YOU RECEIVED THE CHRISTMAS CARD WE SENT YOU?

December 2, 1995

December 12, 1998

December 22, 1996

December 26, 1991

December 21, 1990

FRANKLIN

In 1968, Charlie Brown made a new friend at the beach. Franklin goes to a different school in town, where he is good friends with Peppermint Patty and Marcie. He plays against Charlie Brown on Peppermint Patty's baseball team, but the rivalry doesn't get in the way of their friendship— he is always invited to the Christmas party. During the year, Franklin goes to the movies with the rest of the PEANUTS gang and he and Charlie Brown have long talks about their grampas.

November 17, 1990

12-25 © 1990 United Feature Syndicate, Inc.

December 25, 1990

December 23, 1990

December 24, 1990

SPIKE

Snoopy and his brother Spike were separated as puppies at the Daisy Hill Puppy Farm. While Snoopy took the traditional path after graduation and went to live with Charlie Brown, Spike moved to the desert, where he gets along on his own with the company of "Joe Cactus" and several friendly tumbleweeds. Spike always celebrates Christmas, despite the distinct lack of snow in the desert and he and Snoopy exchange Christmas cards annually.

"ONE OF THE GREAT JOYS OF LIFE IS SITTING BY YOUR CHRISTMAS TREE WHILE BIG FLUFFY SNOWFLAKES FLOAT GENTLY TO THE GROUND . . . OR A NICE SANDSTORM."

December 24, 1995

I THOUGHT MAYBE I'D GET A DOG FOR CHRISTMAS, BUT I DIDN'T..

January 2, 1996

OWNING A DOG IS A BIG RESPONSIBILITY, RERUN..THEY NEED LOTS OF CARE..

© 1995 United Feature Syndicate, Inc.

AND THEY NEED A LOT OF COMFORTING..

1-2-96

December 1, 1997

November 27, 1992

November 21, 1990

December 25, 1994

November 28, 1995

December 8, 1998

Charles Schulz (1922–2000)

"Someday, Charles, you're going to be an artist," his kindergarten teacher once told him. She probably didn't know how prophetic those words would be, but Charles "Sparky" Schulz grew up to become one of the most recognized names in comics.

Born to a barber in Minnesota, Charles Schulz grew up with dreams of writing his own comic strip. After admirable service in World War II, he returned to his passion, drawing, and he took a position as a teacher with his alma mater, Art Instruction Schools. While there, Schulz further honed his skills and met many of the people who would inspire his future work (including a friend named Charlie Brown and a girl with red hair who broke his heart).

Soon he was creating his own comic, which he called "L'il Folks" (it featured a younger Charlie Brown). The *Saturday Evening Post* printed several single comic panels, and the *St. Paul Pioneer Press* made it a weekly feature. "L'il Folks" became the focus of Schulz's career. After expanding it from a single panel to a strip format, he signed a five-year contract with United Feature Syndicate and began his lifelong dream: he was a full-time cartoonist. Because of legal issues surrounding the name "L'il Folks"—"Little Folks" and "L'il Abner" already existed—the strip was renamed PEANUTS, much to Schulz's displeasure.

Over the next fifty years, the world grew to love Charlie Brown, Snoopy, Linus and even Lucy. PEANUTS fans know the characters as well as they know their families, sharing in their losses as well as their triumphs. Every time Charlie Brown missed the football (thanks to Lucy's shenanigans), we missed it, too. When Linus awaited the arrival of the Great Pumpkin, we were out there in the pumpkin patch with him. As Snoopy flew through the air fighting The Red Baron, we flew right alongside him. By mixing humor, friendship, love and life, Charles Schulz made PEANUTS one of the longest-running, most popular comics of all time—and no one but Schulz himself ever drew a panel.

PEANUTS remained Schulz's focus throughout his life, and it became the most popular comic strip ever. It has been published in 21 languages, *in* more than 2,600 newspapers, and has spawned dozens of books, over 50 television specials and even a Broadway musical. *The Joy of a Peanuts Christmas* is Schulz's classic collection of holiday strips, a tribute Hallmark is proud to sponsor.

Charles Schulz died on February 12, 2000, in Santa Rosa, California at the age of 77—only hours before his last original PEANUTS strip was scheduled to appear in Sunday newspapers.